THE OFFICIAL POKéMON Handbook #2

SCHOLASTIC INC.
New York   Toronto   London   Auckland   Sydney
Mexico City   New Delhi   Hong Kong

To Trevor, thanks for all your help.
And to my cousins,
Nicholas and Michael.

ISBN 0-439-15422-7

12   11   10   9   8   7   6   5   4   3   2   1/2   3   4   5   6

Printed in the U.S.A.

First Scholastic printing, January 2001

A WORD FROM PROFESSOR OAK

Greetings, Pokémon trainers! I am Professor Oak, a Pokémon scientist. I spend my time studying and learning about Pokémon and how they behave.

I have exciting news to share with you: many brand-new Pokémon have been discovered all over the world by trainers like you. Those in the western territories report sighting new Pokémon like Totodile, Chikorita, and Cyndaquil.

Pokémon experts like myself need your help to learn everything we can about these new and unusual Pokémon. We have already gathered much useful information, but we need more. That's why it's important for you to update your Pokédex.

Your Official Pokémon Handbook: Gold and Silver Edition contains all of the up-to-the-minute info on the top 33 brand-new Pokémon. It's everything you'll need to know to spot, catch, and train these unique new Pokémon.

Your mission: Be the best Pokémon trainer you can be. You may even discover some never-before-seen Pokémon of your own.

Read up. Stock up on Poké Balls. And catch 'em all!

—Professor Oak

Who's That Pokémon?

Get ready for evolution next — some of the brand-new Pokémon are evolutions of some of the original 150 Pokémon.

Thought Chansey and Scyther never changed? Guess again. They evolve into Blissey and Scizor. Thought Slowpoke could only evolve into Slowbro? Now we know that if Shellder clamps onto Slowpoke's head instead of its tail, Slowpoke will evolve into the brand-new, super-smart Pokémon, Slowking.

Ready for another surprise? Some of the new 33 Pokémon are pre-evolutions of original Pokémon. That means the new Pokémon came first. New Pokémon Elekid actually evolves into Electabuzz. Recently discovered Cleffa evolves into Clefairy. And the just found Igglybuff evolves into favorite Pokémon songster, Jigglypuff!

• EVOLUTION

Just like people, Pokémon don't stay the same forever. As they learn and grow, most Pokémon change form. They evolve! Most Pokémon go through one or two evolutions. After a while, Pokémon stop evolving — but they never stop learning and getting stronger.

There are two basic ways a Pokémon can evolve or change form:

1) **With experience.** With good training, Pokémon can learn new attacks and defense moves, get stronger and smarter. The more a Pokémon competes, the more it will learn and the quicker it will evolve.
2) **With special stones.** Some Pokémon cannot evolve without special stones like the Moon Stone or Thunder Stone. Once you have the stone, you can use it to evolve your Pokémon whenever you want.

New Poké Balls!
Get in Gear!

Don't forget to stock up on Poké Balls before heading out on your training journey. You'll need them to catch new Pokémon.

There are lots of cool new Poké Balls out there, but the most mysterious is the GS Ball. Unlike regular Poké Balls, which are red and white, this ball is gold on top and silver on bottom. Professor Oak received the ball from his friend Professor Ivy, who lives in the Orange Islands. Professor Oak sent young Pokémon trainer Ash Ketchum to Professor Ivy's lab on Valencia Island to pick it up.

Why didn't Professor Ivy just transport the ball to Professor Oak's lab like a regular Poké Ball? Can't be done. And what's even stranger? No one can figure out how to open the GS Ball! Professor Ivy and her assistants tried using buzz saws, hammers, crowbars, hacksaws, power drills, and lasers. Nothing worked. So no one knows what is inside.

No one even knows who made it or why. So, Ash is on a new mission to take the ball to a famous Poké Ball designer named Kurt. He's from Azalea Town in the western territories.

What mysteries does the GS Ball hold? Could a never-before-seen Pokémon be inside? Will you be the Pokémon trainer who reveals the mystery of the GS Ball?

Poké Ball Power

Poké Balls are what you carry your Pokémon around in while you are training them. Only one Pokémon fits in each ball. You can also use Poké Balls to catch new wild Pokémon. Different Poké Balls work best to catch different Pokémon. Choose which Poké Ball you will use depending on the situation you face.

Some Pokémon are common. There are tons of Mareep. But other Pokémon, like Ho-oh and Lugia, are so rare, there is only one of each.

New Pokémon Eggs

Did you know that Togepi is not the only Pokémon that hatched from an egg? Now, there are more! Here's what you need to know about them.

How do you get a new, young Pokémon? Just leave a boy and girl of the same Pokémon at the nearest Pokémon Breeding Center for a while. (Yes — Pokémon can be male or female.) When you return you'll have a brand-new Pokémon. For example, bring in two Jigglypuff, two Electabuzz, or two Clefairy, and head home with a new Igglybuff, Cleffa, or Elekid.

Take note: This might not work with all Pokémon, so get the details before you leave your Pokémon at any breeding center.

No breeding center nearby? Maybe you'll be lucky enough to find a Pokémon egg. Then you can hatch it yourself — just like Ash Ketchum and his friends did with the Togepi egg they found in Grandfather Canyon.

New Type:
The Feel of Steel

Heads up: Team Rocket has been known to scam Pokémon trainers by pretending to run phony breeding centers. Trainers drop off their Pokémon, and when they come back to pick them up — the entire center is gone and their beloved Pokémon are being shipped off to Giovanni, head of the evil Team Rocket enterprise.

Up until now there have been fifteen different types of Pokémon — Bug, Dragon, Electric, Fighting, Fire, Flying, Ghost, Grass, Ground, Ice, Normal, Poison, Psychic, Rock, and Water. Get ready for this — there are two brand-new types of Pokémon, Steel and Dark. Scizor, the evolved form of Scyther, is a combination Steel and Bug Type. It's built to last and tough to beat. It can stand up to many different kinds of attacks.

The Johto Journeys

As you've seen, the world of Pokémon just got bigger. Aside from the new Pokémon facts you've just learned, there are also new lands to explore, new adventures to be had, and new badges to win. Many of the new Pokémon have been spotted in the western territories, just west of Pallet Town. If you want to check out the latest and greatest in the world of Pokémon, head west young Pokémon trainer and take a Johto journey.

The Western Territories Have a League of Their Own: The Johto League

If you want to be a licensed Pokémon trainer, you have to compete in a Pokémon League. The league sets the rules of battle, and gives each trainer his/her first Pokémon and a Pokédex.

A Pokédex is a handheld computer that contains everything you need to know about Pokémon. Every time you spot a new Pokémon, your Pokédex will have the INFO to describe the Pokémon's character, abilities, and where the Pokémon likes to live.

Each league has its own set of rules, different lands to explore, and different badges to earn. Trainers earn badges by competing in Pokémon battles in gyms all over the world.

There are two main leagues-the Indigo League and the Johto League. The Indigo League is the most well-known of all Pokémon Leagues. Many trainers start out in this league. These trainers compete in gyms in towns and cities like Cerulean City and Cinnabar Island in the lands east of the Indigo Plateau.

The second league is the Johto League. New trainers starting their Pokémon journeys in the western territories can sign up to compete in this league. All they have to do is register at the Pokémon Center in New BarkTown. Then they can pick up their very first Pokémon at the lab of Professor Elm. The Johto League territory begins where the Indigo League territory ends-just west of the Indigo Plateau.

Can't decide which league is right for you? You can compete in both. Once you have earned badges in one league, you can travel to the other one and compete for new badges in new lands.

Badge Blowout

No matter what Pokémon League you join, you will earn a badge each time you defeat a Gym Leader in competition. The rules for earning badges vary from league to league and sometimes from gym to gym. But one thing remains the same: A badge is an important sign of your skill as a Pokémon trainer. It shows that you know enough about Pokémon to defeat a skilled trainer in a one-on-one competition. It also shows that your Pokémon are willing to step up to the plate for you. It's a sign that you've earned their respect and friendship.

The Winner's Cup

The Indigo and Johto Leagues aren't the only Pokémon Leagues around. The Orange Islands have a Pokémon League as well. If a trainer earns four badges in the Orange League and goes on to win the championship tournament, that trainer takes home the Orange League Winner's Cup.

How does the Johto League match up to the Indigo League?

Many trainers starting out in the **INDIGO LEAGUE** begin their journeys at Professor Oak's lab in Pallet Town. There, they can choose their first Pokémon from:

Bulbasaur
#01
Grass and Poison Type

Charmander
#04
Fire Type

Squirtle
#07
Water Type

Many trainers in the **JOHTO LEAGUE** begin their journeys at Professor Elm's lab in New Bark Town. They can choose to start out with:

Chikorita
#152
Grass Type

Cyndaquil
#155
Fire Type

Totodile
#158
Water Type

	JOHTO LEAGUE	INDIGO LEAGUE
Number of badges to earn:	At least 8	At least 8
Earning eight badges qualifies trainers to battle in:	The Johto League Championship	The Pokémon League Tournament
Pokémon gyms:	Johto League trainers battle for badges like the Zephyr Badge and the Hive Badge in places like Violet City Gym and Azalea Town Gym.	Indigo League trainers battle for badges like the Cascade Badge and Earth Badge in places like the Cerulean City Gym or the Viridian City Gym.

With all the experience you gain competing in either the Johto League or the Indigo League, you're sure to become a Pokémon Master in no time!

When Team Rocket stole a Totodile from Professor Elm's lab in New Bark Town, Officer Jenny's Arcanine was on the case. It followed the scent left on a Totodile footprint straight to Team Rocket's hideout.

TYPE CASTING (WHAT'S YOUR TYPE?)

Every Pokémon has a type — like Grass, Water, and Fire. Type tells you a lot about a Pokémon, including what moves it will use in battle, and where it likes to live. For example, Fire Pokémon usually enjoy hot, dry places like volcanoes. They may use attacks such as Flamethrower or Fire Spin. Grass Pokémon prefer to get tons of sunlight. Grass Types use attacks like Vine Whip and Razor Leaf.

Type also helps you figure out which kind of Pokémon will do well in a battle against another type. Water dampens Fire, and Fire scorches Grass. Flying Types have an advantage over Ground Types. But Ground Types take the charge out of Electric Types.

Each type has a color in this book. If a Pokémon has two colors, it has two types. Check out the top corner of each page to see that Pokémon's type.

There are now seventeen different types including two brand-new types — Steel and Dark. The Dark Type is so new and mysterious, scientists are keeping all details about it top secret.

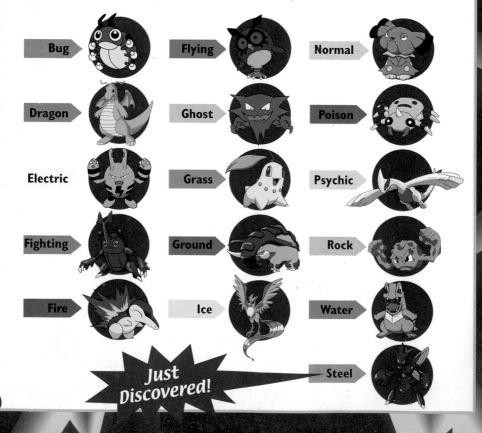

Bug   Flying   Normal

Dragon   Ghost   Poison

Electric   Grass   Psychic

Fighting   Ground   Rock

Fire   Ice   Water

Just Discovered!   Steel

WHAT'S YOUR TYPE?

When Pokémon trainers like Ash Ketchum are going for a badge or facing off against another trainer, they think about which type of Pokémon might do well against their opponent's Pokémon. The following type chart shows you the types of 184 Pokémon. It includes the 33 brand-new Pokémon and all original 151 Pokémon. Use this chart as a quick guide to Pokémon type.

FIRE

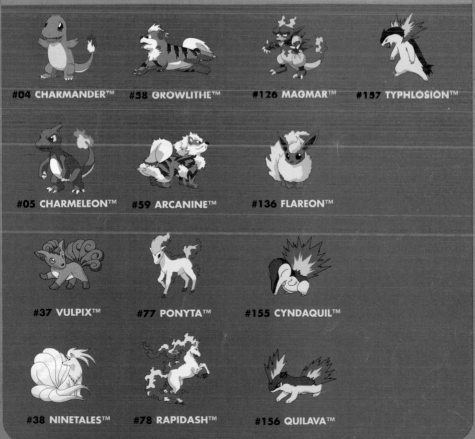

#04 CHARMANDER™   #58 GROWLITHE™   #126 MAGMAR™   #157 TYPHLOSION™

#05 CHARMELEON™   #59 ARCANINE™   #136 FLAREON™

#37 VULPIX™   #77 PONYTA™   #155 CYNDAQUIL™

#38 NINETALES™   #78 RAPIDASH™   #156 QUILAVA™

TYPES

POISON

#23 EKANS™

#33 NIDORINO™

#24 ARBOK™

#88 GRIMER™

#29 NIDORAN™ ♀

#89 MUK™

#30 NIDORINA™

#109 KOFFING™

#32 NIDORAN™ ♂

#110 WEEZING™

ELECTRIC

#25 PIKACHU™

#125 ELECTABUZZ™

#26 RAICHU™

#135 JOLTEON™

#100 VOLTORB™

#179 MAREEP™

#101 ELECTRODE™

#239 ELEKID™

BUG

#10 CATERPIE™

#11 METAPOD™

#127 PINSIR™

TYPES

PSYCHIC

#63 ABRA™

#97 HYPNO™

#64 KADABRA™

#122 MR. MIME™

#65 ALAKAZAM™

#150 MEWTWO™

#96 DROWZEE™

#151 MEW™

GROUND

#27 SANDSHREW™

#104 CUBONE™

#28 SANDSLASH™

#105 MAROWAK™

#50 DIGLETT™

#232 DONPHAN™

#51 DUGTRIO™

GRASS

#114 TANGELA™

#153 BAYLEEF™

#182 BELLOSSOM™

#152 CHIKORITA™

#154 MEGANIUM™

#192 SUNFLORA™

13

TYPES

NORMAL

 #19 RATTATA™

 #52 MEOWTH™

 #132 DITTO™

 #174 IGGLYBUFF™

 #20 RATICATE™

#53 PERSIAN™

 #133 EEVEE™

 #175 TOGEPI™

 #35 CLEFAIRY™

#108 LICKITUNG™

 #137 PORYGON™

 #209 SNUBBULL™

 #36 CLEFABLE™

#113 CHANSEY™

 #143 SNORLAX™

 #234 STANTLER™

 #39 JIGGLYPUFF™

#115 KANGASKHAN™

 #161 SENTRET™

 #242 BLISSEY™

#40 WIGGLYTUFF™

#128 TAUROS™

 #173 CLEFFA™

TYPES

WATER

#07 SQUIRTLE™

#86 SEEL™

#119 SEAKING™

#158 TOTODILE™

#08 WARTORTLE™

#90 SHELLDER™

#120 STARYU™

#159 CROCONAW™

#09 BLASTOISE™

#98 KRABBY™

#129 MAGIKARP™

#160 FERALIGATR™

#54 PSYDUCK™

#99 KINGLER™

#134 VAPOREON™

#183 MARILL™

#55 GOLDUCK™

#116 HORSEA™

DRAGON

#147 DRATINI™ #148 DRAGONAIR™

#60 POLIWAG™

#117 SEADRA™

#61 POLIWHIRL™

#118 GOLDEEN™

TYPES

FIGHTING

#56 MANKEY™

#67 MACHOKE™

#107 HITMONCHAN™

#57 PRIMEAPE™

#68 MACHAMP™

#66 MACHOP™

#106 HITMONLEE™

BUG/ POISON

#13 WEEDLE™

#14 KAKUNA™

#15 BEEDRILL™

#48 VENONAT™

#49 VENOMOTH™

#167 SPINARAK™

BUG/ FLYING

#12 BUTTERFREE™

#123 SCYTHER™

#165 LEDYBA™

BUG/ GRASS

#46 PARAS™

#47 PARASECT™

BUG/ FIGHTING

#214 HERACROSS™

BUG/ STEEL

#212 SCIZOR™

TYPES

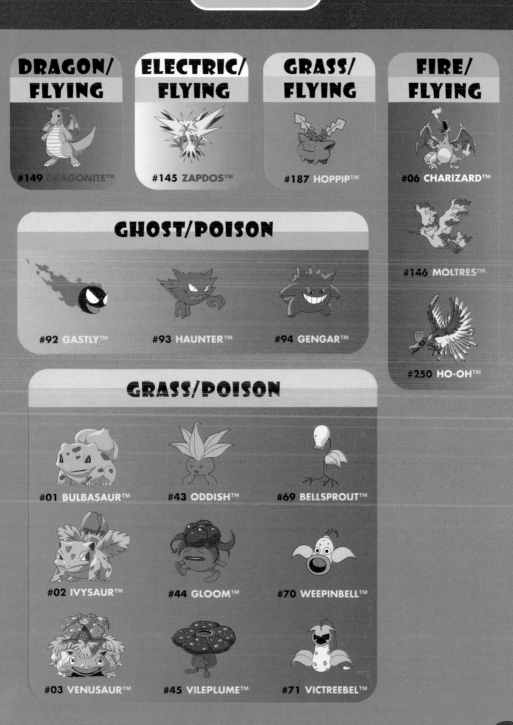

DRAGON/ FLYING

#149 DRAGONITE™

ELECTRIC/ FLYING

#145 ZAPDOS™

GRASS/ FLYING

#187 HOPPIP™

FIRE/ FLYING

#06 CHARIZARD™

#146 MOLTRES™

#250 HO-OH™

GHOST/POISON

#92 GASTLY™

#93 HAUNTER™

#94 GENGAR™

GRASS/POISON

#01 BULBASAUR™

#43 ODDISH™

#69 BELLSPROUT™

#02 IVYSAUR™

#44 GLOOM™

#70 WEEPINBELL™

#03 VENUSAUR™

#45 VILEPLUME™

#71 VICTREEBEL™

TYPES

GRASS/ PSYCHIC

#102 EXEGGCUTE™

#103 EXEGGUTOR™

GROUND/ FLYING

#207 GLIGAR™

ICE/ FLYING

#144 ARTICUNO™

NORMAL/FLYING

#16 PIDGEY™

#21 SPEAROW™

#84 DODUO™

#17 PIDGEOTTO™

#22 FEAROW™

#85 DODRIO™

#18 PIDGEOT™

#83 FARFETCH'D™

#163 HOOTHOOT™

GROUND/ ROCK

#111 RHYHORN™

#112 RHYDON™

PSYCHIC/ FLYING

#249 LUGIA™

ICE/ PSYCHIC

#124 JYNX™

TYPES

POISON/ GROUND

#31 NIDOQUEEN™

#34 NIDOKING™

ROCK/ FLYING

#142 AERODACTYL™

POISON/ FLYING

#41 ZUBAT™

#42 GOLBAT™

WATER/ FIGHTING

#62 POLIWRATH™

WATER/ FLYING

#130 GYARADOS™

ROCK/WATER

#138 OMANYTE™

#140 KABUTO™

#139 OMASTAR™

#141 KABUTOPS™

ROCK/GROUND

#74 GEODUDE™

#76 GOLEM™

#75 GRAVELER™

#95 ONIX™

TYPES

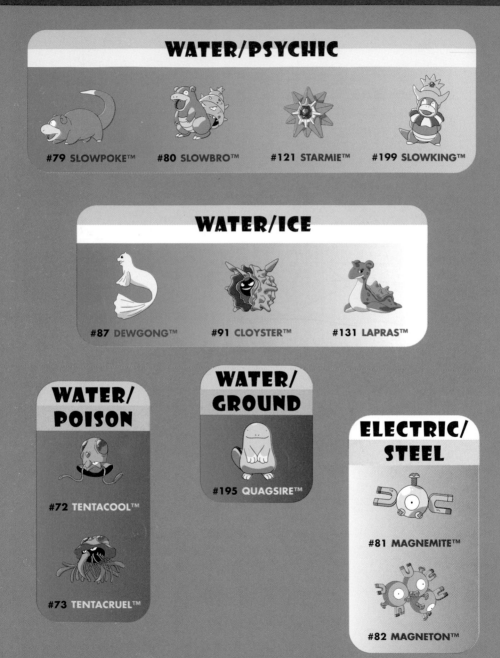

WATER/PSYCHIC

#79 SLOWPOKE™ #80 SLOWBRO™ #121 STARMIE™ #199 SLOWKING™

WATER/ICE

#87 DEWGONG™ #91 CLOYSTER™ #131 LAPRAS™

WATER/ POISON

#72 TENTACOOL™

#73 TENTACRUEL™

WATER/ GROUND

#195 QUAGSIRE™

ELECTRIC/ STEEL

#81 MAGNEMITE™

#82 MAGNETON™

IT'S TIME FOR A POKéDEX UPGRADE

Pokémon experts like Professor Oak have updated your Pokédex. It's got new information and a brand-new look. Use it as a quick guide to help you train your Pokémon.

Check it out!

#152 CHIKORITA™

Leaf Pokémon

HOW TO SAY IT:
CHICK-OR-*EEE*-TUH

TYPE:
GRASS

HEIGHT:
2' 11"

WEIGHT:
14 LBS.

ATTACKS:
TACKLE, GROWL,
RAZOR LEAF,
REFLECT,
POISON POWDER,
TEMPERATURE

EVOLUTION:
CHIKORITA EVOLVES
INTO BAYLEEF.

Pokédex Pick:

The Chikorita from Violet City in the western territories are known for their spunk. They'll keep fighting even if they know they can't win. They never give up!

A sweet aroma gently wafts from the leaf on Chikorita's head. Chikorita is docile and loves to soak up the sun's rays.

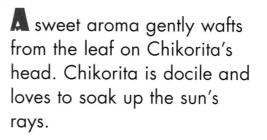

#153 BAYLEEF™

Leaf Pokémon

HOW TO SAY IT:
BAY-LEEF

TYPE:
GRASS

HEIGHT:
3' 11"

WEIGHT:
35 LBS.

ATTACKS:
RAZOR LEAF,
REFLECT,
POISON POWDER,
SYNTHESIS,
BODY SLAM

EVOLUTION:
BAYLEEF EVOLVES
INTO MEGANIUM.

A spicy aroma emanates from around Bayleef's neck. The aroma acts as a stimulant to restore health. Somehow, sniffing it also makes Pokémon want to fight.

#154 MEGANIUM™

Herb Pokémon

HOW TO SAY IT:
MUH-GAY-KNEE-UM

TYPE:
GRASS

HEIGHT:
5' 11"

WEIGHT:
222 LBS.

ATTACKS:
TACKLE, GROWL,
RAZOR LEAF,
SYNTHESIS,
BODY SLAM,
LIGHT SCREEN,
SAFEGUARD,
SOLARBEAM

EVOLUTION:
MEGANIUM IS THE
MOST EVOLVED FORM
OF CHIKORITA AND
BAYLEEF.

Meganium's breath has the power to make dead grass and plants healthy again. The aroma that rises from its petals contains a substance that calms aggressive feelings.

#155 CYNDAQUIL™

Fire Mouse Pokémon

HOW TO SAY IT:
SIN-DA-QWIL

TYPE:
FIRE

HEIGHT:
1' 8"

WEIGHT:
17 LBS.

ATTACKS:
TACKLE, LEER,
SMOKESCREEN,
EMBER

EVOLUTION:
CYNDAQUIL EVOLVES
INTO QUILAVA.

Cyndaquil is timid and always curls itself up in a ball. If attacked, it flares up its back for protection.

Pokédex Pick:

Misty, a trainer from Cerulean City, picked up a Cyndaquil once. Big mistake! It almost charred her hair!

#156 QUILAVA™
Volcano Pokémon

HOW TO SAY IT:
QWI-LAVA

TYPE:
FIRE

HEIGHT:
2' 11"

WEIGHT:
42 LBS.

ATTACKS:
EMBER,
QUICK ATTACK,
FLAME WHEEL

EVOLUTION:
QUILAVA EVOLVES
INTO TYPHLOSION.

This Pokémon is fully covered by nonflammable fur. It can withstand any kind of fire attack. Be careful if it turns its back during battle. It means that it will attack with the fire on its back.

#157 TYPHLOSION™

Volcano Pokémon

HOW TO SAY IT:
TIE-*FLOW*-SION

TYPE:
FIRE

HEIGHT:
5'7"

WEIGHT:
175 LBS.

ATTACKS:
FLAME WHEEL,
SWIFT,
FLAMETHROWER

EVOLUTION:
TYPHLOSION IS
THE MOST EVOLVED
FORM OF CYNDAQUIL
AND QUILAVA

Typhlosion has a secret, devastating move. It rubs its blazing fur together to cause huge explosions. If its rage peaks, Typhlosion becomes so hot that anything that touches it will instantly go up in flames.

#158 TOTODILE™

Big Jaw Pokémon

HOW TO SAY IT:
TOT-O-DILE

TYPE:
WATER

HEIGHT:
2'

WEIGHT:
21 LBS.

ATTACKS:
SCRATCH,
LEER, RAGE,
WATER GUN

EVOLUTION:
TOTODILE EVOLVES
INTO CROCONAW.

Totodile's well-developed jaws are powerful and capable of crushing any-thing. Even its trainer has to be careful.

Pokédex Pick:

When Team Rocket tried to kidnap a Totodile, the Water Pokémon clamped its crushing jaws on Jessie's hair. Then Totodile used its Water Gun Attack to send Jessie, James, and Meowth blasting off again!

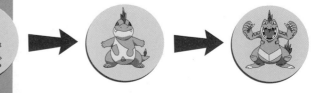

HOW TO SAY IT:
CROCK-O-NAW

TYPE:
WATER

HEIGHT:
3'7"

WEIGHT:
55 LBS.

ATTACKS:
RAGE, WATER GUN,
BITE, SCARY FACE

EVOLUTION:
CROCONAW EVOLVES
INTO FERALIGATR.

Croconaw opens its huge jaws wide when attacking. If it loses a fang while biting, a new one grows back in place. There are always 48 fangs lining its mouth.

#160 FERALIGATR™

Big Jaw Pokémon

HOW TO SAY IT:
FUR-AL-I-GAY-TER

TYPE:
WATER

HEIGHT:
7' 7"

WEIGHT:
196 LBS.

ATTACKS:
BITE, SCARY FACE,
SLASH, SCREECH,
HYDRO PUMP

EVOLUTION:
FERALIGATR IS THE
MOST EVOLVED FORM
OF TOTODILE AND
CROCONAW.

It is hard for Feraligatr to support its own weight out of water, so it gets down on all fours. But it moves fast. When Feraligatr bites with its massive and powerful jaws, it shakes its head and savagely tears up its victim.

#161 SENTRET™

Scout Pokémon

Sentret stands on its tail so it can see a long way. If it spots an enemy, it cries loudly to warn its kind. A very cautious Pokémon, Sentret raises itself up using its tail to get a better view of its surroundings.

#163 HOOTHOOT™

Owl Pokémon

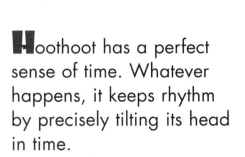

HOW TO SAY IT:
HOOT-HOOT

TYPE:
NORMAL /FLYING

HEIGHT:
2' 4"

WEIGHT:
47 LBS.

ATTACKS:
TACKLE, GROWL,
FORESIGHT, PECK

EVOLUTION:
HOOTHOOT EVOLVES
INTO A NEW
POKÉMON.

Hoothoot has a perfect sense of time. Whatever happens, it keeps rhythm by precisely tilting its head in time.

Pokédex Pick:

Hagatha rents Hoothoot to help travelers find their way through forests. They shoot red laser beams from their eyes to make the illusions created by prankster Ghost Pokémon like Gastly and Haunter disappear. Hoothoot isn't afraid of any Ghost Pokémon.

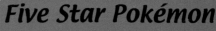

Five Star Pokémon

HOW TO SAY IT:
LAY-DEE-BAH

TYPE:
BUG/FLYING

HEIGHT:
3' 3"

WEIGHT:
24 LBS.

ATTACKS:
TACKLE,
SUPERSONIC,
COMET PUNCH

EVOLUTION:
LEDYBA EVOLVES
INTO A NEW
POKÉMON.

When the weather turns cold, lots of Ledyba gather from everywhere to cluster and keep one another warm. Ledyba is very timid. It will be afraid to move if it is alone. But it will be active if it is in a group.

Pokédex Pick:

Ledyba first took to the skies in *Pikachu's Rescue Adventure* when they caught Pikachu and its airborne friends on their backs. Then the Ledyba took their new friends flying through a whole new world.

#167 SPINARAK™

Stringspit Pokémon

HOW TO SAY IT:
SPIN-A-RACK

TYPE:
BUG/POISON

HEIGHT:
1' 8"

WEIGHT:
19 LBS.

ATTACKS:
POISON STING,
STRING SHOT,
SCARY FACE,
CONSTRICT,
NIGHT SHADE

EVOLUTION:
SPINARAK EVOLVES
INTO A NEW
POKÉMON.

Spinarak spins a web using fine, but durable thread. It then waits patiently for prey to be trapped. Spinarak lies in the same pose for days in its web, waiting for its unsuspecting prey to wander close.

Pokédex Pick:

Police officers often use Spinarak to set up roadblocks and catch thieves. Officer Jenny asks Spinarak to spin their webs in the middle of the road. Then, passing Pokémon thieves like Team Rocket get trapped in the sticky nets.

#173 CLEFFA™
Starshape Pokémon

HOW TO SAY IT:
CLEFF-AH

TYPE:
NORMAL

HEIGHT:
1'

WEIGHT:
7 LBS.

ATTACKS:
**POUND, CHARM,
ENCORE, SING,
SWEET KISS**

EVOLUTION:
**CLEFFA EVOLVES
INTO CLEFAIRY.**

When numerous meteors illuminate the night sky, sightings of Cleffa strangely increase. Because of its unusual, starlike silhouette, people believe that Cleffa came to earth on a meteor.

Balloon Pokémon

HOW TO SAY IT:
IGG-LEE-BUFF

TYPE:
NORMAL

HEIGHT:
1'

WEIGHT:
2 LBS.

ATTACKS:
SING, CHARM,
DEFENSE CURL,
POUND, SWEET KISS

EVOLUTION:
IGGLYBUFF EVOLVES
INTO JIGGLYPUFF.

Igglybuff's extremely flexible and elastic body makes it bounce continuously — anytime, anywhere. It has a very soft body. If it starts to roll, it will bounce all over and be impossible to stop.

#175 TOGEPI™
Spike Ball Pokémon

HOW TO SAY IT:
TOE-GAH-PEE

TYPE:
NORMAL

HEIGHT:
1'

WEIGHT:
3 LBS.

ATTACKS:
**CHARM,
METRONOME,
SWEET KISS,
ENCORE,
SAFEGUARD**

EVOLUTION:
**TOGEPI EVOLVES
INTO A NEW
POKÉMON.**

A proverb claims that happiness will come to anyone who can make a sleeping Togepi stand up. The shell seems to be filled with joy. It is said that Togepi will share good luck when treated kindly.

Pokédex Pick:
Some Togepi are afraid of thunder. They hide in their egg shells during storms.

Wool Pokémon

HOW TO SAY IT:
MA-REEP

TYPE:
ELECTRIC

HEIGHT:
2'

WEIGHT:
17 LBS.

ATTACKS:
TACKLE, GROWL, THUNDERSHOCK

EVOLUTION:
MAREEP EVOLVES INTO A NEW POKÉMON.

Pokédex Pick:

One town in the western territories holds an annual carnival to thank the Mareep for providing them with the finest wool. It's quite an event. There are Pokémon battle contests and Mareep-judging, too. But before you head on down, take note: Only if you live there, are you allowed to compete. Mareep absorb electricity from storms. It keeps them strong and helps keep their fleeces at their most beautiful.

Mareep's fleece grows continually. In the summer, the fleece is fully shed, but it grows back in a week. If static electricity builds in its body, Mareep's fleece doubles in volume. Touching it will shock you.

Flower Pokémon

HOW TO SAY IT:
BELL-*AWE*-SUM

TYPE:
GRASS

HEIGHT:
1' 4"

WEIGHT:
13 LBS.

ATTACKS:
ABSORB,
SWEET SCENT,
STUN SPORE,
PETAL DANCE,
SOLARBEAM

EVOLUTION:
BELLOSSOM IS AN
EVOLVED FORM
OF GLOOM.

Bellossom are plentiful in the tropics. When it dances, Bellossom's petals rub together and make a pleasant ringing sound. Bellossom gather together at times to dance. Some say it is a ritual to summon the sun.

Pokédex Pick:

A group of Bellossom sang and danced for Pikachu and friends in the short cartoon Pikachu's Rescue Adventure.

#183 MARILL™

Aquamouse Pokémon

HOW TO SAY IT:
MARE-ILL

TYPE:
WATER

HEIGHT:
1' 4"

WEIGHT:
19 LBS.

ATTACKS:
TACKLE,
DEFENSE CURL,
TAIL WHIP,
WATER GUN,
ROLLOUT

EVOLUTION:
MARILL EVOLVES
INTO A NEW
POKÉMON.

Pokédex Pick:

Ash Ketchum and friends found a sad and lost Marill in Azalea Town. It cried so loud, even Team Rocket didn't want to snatch it.

The end of Marill's tail serves as a buoy that keeps it from drowning, even in a vicious current. The tip of its tail, which contains oil that is lighter than water, lets Mareep swim without drowning.

Cottonweed Pokémon

HOW TO SAY IT:
HOP-PIP

TYPE:
GRASS/FLYING

HEIGHT:
1' 4"

WEIGHT:
1 LB.

ATTACKS:
SPLASH, SYNTHESIS,
TAIL WHIP, TACKLE,
POISON POWDER,
STUN SPORE

EVOLUTION:
HOPPIP EVOLVES
INTO A NEW
POKÉMON.

Hoppip's body is so light, it must grip the ground firmly with its feet to keep from being blown away. Hoppip also gather in clusters to keep from being blown away by the wind. They do enjoy gentle breezes, though.

#192 SUNFLORA™

Sun Pokémon

HOW TO SAY IT:
SUN-*FLOOR*-UH

TYPE:
GRASS

HEIGHT:
2' 7"

WEIGHT:
19 LBS.

ATTACKS:
POUND,
RAZOR LEAF,
SUNNY DAY,
PETAL DANCE,
SOLARBEAM

EVOLUTION:
SUNFLORA IS THE MOST EVOLVED FORM OF A NEW POKÉMON.

In the daytime, Sunflora rushes about in a hectic manner, but it comes to a complete stop when the sun sets. Sunflora converts sunlight into energy. In the darkness after sunset, it closes its petals and becomes still.

Pokédex Pick:

Bloomingvale is famous for all the Sunflora raised there. They have an annual Sunflora Festival. The trainer with the best-looking, best-trained Sunflora is called the Sunflora Star. Jessie and James made Meowth dress up like a Sunflora and entered him in the festival. They lost, of course!

#195 QUAGSIRE™
Water Fish Pokémon

HOW TO SAY IT:
QWAG-SIRE

TYPE:
WATER/GROUND

HEIGHT:
4' 7"

WEIGHT:
165 LBS.

ATTACKS:
EARTHQUAKE,
RAIN DANCE, MIST,
HAZE, WATER GUN,
SLAM, AMNESIA

EVOLUTION:
QUAGSIRE IS THE
MOST EVOLVED FORM
OF A NEW POKÉMON.

Due to its relaxed and carefree attitude, Quagsire often bumps its head on boulders and boat hulls as it swims. This carefree Pokémon has an easygoing nature.

Pokédex Pick:
The people of Cherrygrove City don't like trainers to catch their wild Quagsire. The Quagsire in Cherrygrove City will only live in very clean waters. So if Quagsire live in a lake, the townspeople know the water is pure enough to drink.

#199 SLOWKING™
Royal Pokémon

HOW TO SAY IT:
SLOW-KING

TYPE:
WATER/PSYCHIC

HEIGHT:
6' 7"

WEIGHT:
175 LBS.

ATTACKS:
CURSE, WATER GUN, CONFUSION, DISABLE, HEADBUTT, SWAGGER

EVOLUTION:
SLOWKING IS AN EVOLVED FORM OF SLOWPOKE.

Pokédex Pick:
In Pokémon the Movie 2000: The Power of One, Slowking was the guardian of a sacred temple on Shamouti Island. It told Ash and friends an ancient legend about the destruction of the world.

When Slowpoke's head was bitten by Shellder, toxins entered Slowpoke's head and unlocked extraordinary power. Slowking has incredible intellect and intuition. Whatever the situation, it remains calm and collected.

#207 GLIGAR™
Flyscorpio Pokémon

HOW TO SAY IT:
GLIE-GAR

TYPE:
GROUND/FLYING

HEIGHT:
3' 7"

WEIGHT:
143 LBS.

ATTACKS:
POISON STING, SAND THROW, BITE, SLASH, SCREECH, GUILLOTINE

EVOLUTION:
GLIGAR DOES NOT EVOLVE.

Gligar usually clings to cliffs. When it spots its prey, it spreads its wings and glides down to attack. Gligar flies straight at its target's face, then clamps down on the startled victim to inject poison.

Pokédex Pick:

Look! Up in the sky! Is it a Pidgeotto? A Charizard? A Dragonite? No. It's super GligarMan! This Pokémon trainer dresses up like his best Pokémon, Gligar, to check the reach of evil, and fill the world with truth and love.

#209 SNUBBULL™

Fairy Pokémon

HOW TO SAY IT:
SNUB-BULL

TYPE:
NORMAL

HEIGHT:
2'

WEIGHT:
17 LBS.

ATTACKS:
SCARY FACE,
TAIL WHIP, CHARM,
BITE, LICK, ROAR

EVOLUTION:
SNUBBULL EVOLVES
INTO A NEW
POKÉMON.

Snubbull has an active, playful nature. Many women like to frolic with it because of its affectionate ways. Although Snubbull looks frightening, it is actually kind and affectionate. It is very popular among women.

Pokédex Pick:

Most Snubbull like to play. Let them run around in the yard and treat them to tasty snacks. One Snubbull tried to run away because it did not like living in the lap of luxury. It needed exercise — not designer clothes!

Scissors Pokémon

HOW TO SAY IT:
SIE-ZOR

TYPE:
BUG/STEEL

HEIGHT:
5 'II"

WEIGHT:
260 LBS.

ATTACKS:
FOCUS ENERGY,
PURSUIT,
FALSE SWIPE,
AGILITY,
METAL CLAW,
SWORDS DANCE,
DOUBLE TEAM

EVOLUTION:
SCIZOR IS THE MOST
EVOLVED FORM OF
SCYTHER.

Scizor's wings are not used for flying. They are flapped at high speed to adjust its body temperature. Scizor swings its eye-patterned pincers up to scare its foes. This makes it look like it has three heads.

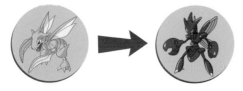

#214 HERACROSS™
Singlehorn Pokémon

HOW TO SAY IT:
HAIR-A-CROSS

TYPE:
BUG/FIGHTING

HEIGHT:
4' 11"

WEIGHT:
119 LBS.

ATTACKS:
HORN ATTACK,
ENDURE,
FURY ATTACK,
COUNTER,
TAKE DOWN,
REVERSAL,
MEGAHORN

EVOLUTION:
HERACROSS
DOES NOT EVOLVE.

Heracross is usually docile. But if disturbed while sipping honey, it chases off the intruder with its horn. This powerful Pokémon thrusts its prized horn under its enemies' bellies, then lifts and throws them.

Pokédex Pick:
Heracross is one of Ash Ketchum's Pokémon.

Armor Pokémon

HOW TO SAY IT:
DON-FAN

TYPE:
GROUND

HEIGHT:
3' 7"

WEIGHT:
265 LBS.

ATTACKS:
TACKLE,
ROLLOUT,
ENDURE,
EARTHQUAKE

EVOLUTION:
DONPHAN IS THE
MOST EVOLVED
FORM OF A NEW
POKÉMON.

Donphan has sharp, hard tusks and a rugged hide. The tusks take a long time to grow. The longer and bigger its tusks, the higher Donphan's rank in the herd. Its Tackle is strong enough to knock down a house.

Pokédex Pick:
Ash Ketchum used his Heracross' Horn Attack to battle a young, wild Donphan. He would have caught Donphan in his Poké Ball, but it belonged to another trainer. Oops! Catching another trainer's Pokémon is NOT allowed.

#234 STANTLER™
Big Horn Pokémon

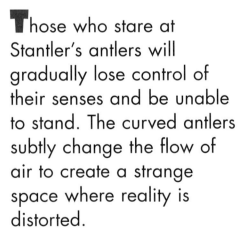

HOW TO SAY IT:
STANT-LER

TYPE:
NORMAL

HEIGHT:
4' 7"

WEIGHT:
157 LBS.

ATTACKS:
HYPNOSIS,
STOMP, SAND
THROW, THRASH,
CONFUSE RAY

EVOLUTION:
STANTLER DOES
NOT EVOLVE.

Pokédex Pick:
One little Stantler can cause big trouble. One lost and lonely young Stantler created a Stantler stampede in a town in the western territories. The fake herd chased Ash Ketchum, Brock, Misty — even Team Rocket. Brock figured out what was going on and helped the frightened Stantler find its family.

Those who stare at Stantler's antlers will gradually lose control of their senses and be unable to stand. The curved antlers subtly change the flow of air to create a strange space where reality is distorted.

#239 ELEKID™

Electric Pokémon

HOW TO SAY IT:
EL-AH-KID

TYPE:
ELECTRIC

HEIGHT:
2'

WEIGHT:
52 LBS.

ATTACKS:
THUNDER PUNCH,
LIGHT SCREEN,
SWIFT, SCREECH

EVOLUTION:
ELEKID EVOLVES
INTO ELECTABUZZ.

Even in the most vicious storm, this Pokémon plays happily when the thunder rumbles in the sky. Elekid rotates its arms to generate electricity, but it tires easily, so it charges up only a little bit.

Pokédex Pick:

In the movie short, Pikachu's Rescue Adventure, Elekid helped save a nest full of Exeggcute and Togepi from the strong winds of a lightning storm. Elekid and Pikachu combined their Thundershock Attacks and aimed them at the storm clouds. The storm ended and the Pokémon were safe.

#242 BLISSEY™

Happiness Pokémon

HOW TO SAY IT:
BLISS-EE

TYPE:
NORMAL

HEIGHT:
4' 11"

WEIGHT:
103 LBS.

ATTACKS:
POUND, SLAP,
EGG RECOVER,
DOUBLE SLAP,
MINIMIZE, SING,
EGG BOMB,
LIGHT SCREEN,
SUBMISSION

EVOLUTION:
BLISSEY IS THE
MOST EVOLVED
FORM OF CHANSEY.

Pokédex Pick:
One Blissey actually
went to nursing
school with Jessie of
Team Rocket. Jessie
failed, but Blissey went
on to become a kind
nurse Pokémon.

Blissey has a very compassionate nature. If it sees a sick Pokémon, it will nurse the sufferer back to health. Anyone who takes even one bite of Blissey's egg becomes unfailingly caring and pleasant to everyone.

#249 LUGIA™

Diving Pokémon

HOW TO SAY IT:
LU-GEE-UH

TYPE:
PSYCHIC/FLYING

HEIGHT:
17' 1"

WEIGHT:
476 LBS.

ATTACKS:
AEROBLAST, MIST,
GUST, HYDRO PUMP,
RAIN DANCE,
WHIRLWIND,
ANCIENT POWER,
FUTURE SIGHT

EVOLUTION:
LUGIA DOES
NOT EVOLVE.

Lugia is said to be a ruler of the seas. It is rumored to have been seen on the night of a ferocious storm. It is said that Lugia quietly spends its time deep at the bottom of the sea because its powers are too strong.

Pokédex Pick:

Lugia made its big screen debut in Pokémon the Movie 2000: The Power of One. It helped Ash Ketchum save the world from ultimate destruction.

#250 HO-OH™

Rainbow Pokémon

HOW TO SAY IT:
HO-OH

TYPE:
FIRE/FLYING

HEIGHT:
12' 6"

WEIGHT:
439 LBS.

ATTACKS:
SACRED FIRE,
NORMAL, MIST,
FIRE BLAST,
SUNNY DAY,
WHIRLWIND,
ANCIENT POWER,
FUTURE SIGHT

EVOLUTION:
HO-OH DOES
NOT EVOLVE.

A legend says that Ho-oh's body glows in seven colors. A rainbow is said to form behind it when it flies. Legends claim this Pokémon flies the world's skies continuously on its magnificent wings.

Pokédex Pick:
Ash Ketchum saw this Pokémon on his very first day as a trainer!

54

POKÉMON HALL OF FAME
CATCH PICTURES OF YOUR FAVORITE POKÉMON IN ACTION.

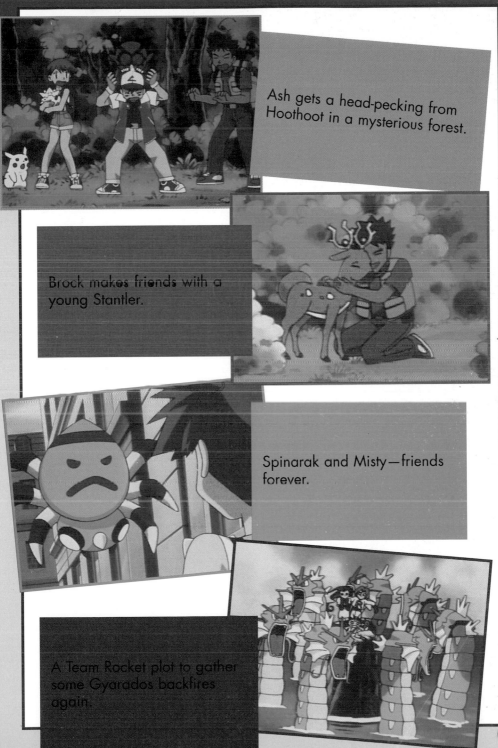

Ash gets a head-pecking from Hoothoot in a mysterious forest.

Brock makes friends with a young Stantler.

Spinarak and Misty—friends forever.

A Team Rocket plot to gather some Gyarados backfires again.

Onix uses Bind to take down Team Rocket's robotic Stantler.

Who caught whom? Totodile chomps Jessie's hair.

Who is that mysterious blue Pokémon?

Growlithe and Pikachu are hot on the trail of Team Rocket.

Marill uses its super-hearing to track a crystal Onix.

Chikorita attacks!

Arbok vs. Blissey. Who will win?

Snack time!
Heracross and Butterfree share the sap from a tree.

POKéMON QUICK PICKS

Electrode are known as the living bomb because they have explosive tempers. Electrode that live in the city are the worst. As more and more Electrode are forced to live in a small space, they stress out. They could explode for the smallest reason. But exploding leaves Electrode so wiped out, they can't even battle. They also can't explode again until their power is recharged.

Most Butterfree and Heracross live peacefully together. They both like to eat the sap from trees.

Dugtrio tunnel through the earth with the greatest of ease.

A master Pokémon thief traveled all over the world snatching Pokémon with the help of his Meowth. Meowth used Pay Day to make a shower of coins appear out of thin air. It scared away anyone who tried to catch them. Well, not everyone. The thief and Meowth were eventually trapped in a sticky Spinarak web.

Team Rocket's Meowth understands all Pokémon language. Ash, Misty, and Brock once used Meowth to find out what was making a Sunflora so unhappy. He's like an official Pokémon translator! So why *was* the Sunflora sad? Because all of the other Sunflora it used to play with in the park were gone.

Since Bulbasaur is a Grass Pokémon just like Chikorita, it should be able to follow Chikorita's sweet scent.

Brock's Rockin' Advice: "When you want to get close to a Pokémon, the best way is to copy its behavior. Then you won't scare it away."

"I think understanding your Pokémon's feelings is more important than anything else. In battles, or anywhere else, really, your Pokémon always works for you, right? It shouldn't be a one-way road."
— Ash Ketchum, Pokémon Trainer

Here's some training strategy: During a battle with a Mareep, Ash had Pikachu stop using electricity because it was getting worn down. He concentrated on agility moves instead. If Pikachu had continued using electricity, it would have fainted.

Pokémon learn to express themselves in many different ways. One way is through dance. The Bellossom in Florando use dance moves to win battles all the time. Dance steps are just like a fighter's footwork. Rhythm is important in battling, too.

Ash's Pikachu and Chikorita became fast friends. But Chikorita gets jealous when Ash pays too much attention to other Pokémon.

Gastly and Haunter can create holograms or illusions of other Pokémon to scare Pokémon trainers in dark, eerie forests.

Both Growlithe and Spinarak help Officer Jenny catch Pokémon thieves like Team Rocket.

Diglett, the mole Pokémon, are known for digging complicated tunnels just below the surface of the earth. One town had an explosive Electrode problem. The people used Diglett's Dig Attack to take the Electrode down underground. The Electrode were led through the tunnels and out to a prairie where they could live stress-free.

Welcome to the Charicific Valley

The Charicific Valley is a well-known Charizard habitat. The Charizard in Charicific Valley are wild. They don't rely on humans to become stronger. Instead they compete against one another. They are the same species, with the same goal, encouraging one another and always growing. All that friendly competition makes Charizard from the Charicific Valley bigger and stronger than normal, wild Charizard.

Both Zubat and Ledyba use Supersonic waves to help them stay on course when flying. It's like a built-in radar system.

When Team Rocket stole all the sap from the trees in the Pinsir forest, the Pinsir were forced to invade the Heracross' territory for food.

Most trainers make their Eevee evolve right away. But not Professor Oak's grandson, Gary. He spent a lot of time training his Eevee for battle. When Gary's Eevee battled Ash Ketchum's Pikachu, it didn't seem to take any damage at all. Pikachu's Agility and Thunder were no match for Eevee's speed. Eevee defeated Pikachu with its Double Team, Take Down, and Skull Bash Attacks.

Voltorb have explosive personalities. But Voltorbs' true identity is hidden inside an outer shell. Take extreme caution if you want to catch one. Voltorb are known to explode without warning.

Mareep herders sometimes use Raichu like sheep dogs to keep herds of Mareep in line. Raichu uses its Thunder to give the Mareep a charge.

Hoothoot used its eye-beams to reveal a gang of Gengar and Haunter in the forest. Then, Bulbasaur and Pikachu scared Gengar and Haunter off with a Vine Whip and a Thundershock.

Bulbasaur gets grumpy when Heracross tries to eat the pollen from its plant bulb.

Misty's Poliwag helped save a young Donphan from Team Rocket's evil clutches. Poliwag used a Doubleslap followed by a Bubble Attack to topple James' Victreebel.

Arbok are easily charmed by the sound of a flute. Jessie wanted her Arbok to attack a group of Ledyba during one tense battle, but Arbok was too busy moving to the music.

If Pokémon don't get enough attention, they become sad. Sometimes Pokémon even become jealous if you give another Pokémon more care or training. Ash's Chikorita ran away because it was jealous of all the care Ash gave Pikachu.

Ash Ketchum's mom has a Mr. Mime to help out around the house. Mr. Mime once used his Light Screen to protect her herb garden from a Team Rocket Attack.

Pokémon updates are flooding in every day. New Pokémon have been spotted. Strange Pokémon are battling one another. Pokémon experts are rushing to make sense of the reports from Pokémon trainers around the world. Here's the inside scoop straight from the lab of Professor Oak — the world's most famous Pokémon expert.

What can we expect from the rest of the 100 new Pokémon?

EVOLUTION NEXT

• **More pre-evolutions** — including the super cute pre-evolutions of Pikachu, Jynx, and Magmar.

• **Some of your favorite new Pokémon evolve into even newer Pokémon** — Sentret, Hoothoot, Spinarak, Togepi, Mareep, Marill, Hoppip, and Snubbull will all have evolutions in the next batch of new Pokémon.

• **Pre-evolutions of some of your favorite new Pokémon like Sunflora, Quagsire, and Donphan.**

• **New evolutions of more of the original 150 Pokémon like Eevee, Porygon, and Seadra.**

• **More cool new Pokémon**
There are Pokémon that look like bats, bugs, monkeys, and totem poles. Others resemble twigs, frogs, stingrays, dogs, bears, turtles, pine cones, or water droplets. There are even some that look like computer symbols, skeletal snakes, wooly mammoths, cows, aliens, ghostly apparitions, birds, monsters, and more!

They have antennae and/or, tails, fins, fur, horns, flippers, feathers, fire-breath, scales, horns, fangs, claws. Some have eyes on their chests, stripes, spots, wings, flowers, bubbles, shells. Others show off forked tails, slime, trunks, paws, claws, spikes, and even two heads. Some are made of rocks, vapor, grass, spores, or goo.

They are psychic, fiery, explosive, strong, poisonous, mysterious — and cute!

They will shock, mystify, paralyze, blow you away, and keep you on your toes.

They pack a punch. Some conduct electricity, spark in the dark, bring you good luck, crumble when touched, jump, bounce, or fly. Some have tails that shine with bright lights and can guide people through the darkness. Others store electricity, hear distant sounds, croak, hang from their tails, fly at high speeds, shatter glass, secrete poisonous venom, sense when an enemy will attack, bring bad luck, play tricks on people, swell, roll into a ball, or hide in a shell at the first sign of danger. Others shoot poison needles, chase enemies, never give up, bite enemies with the heads on their tails, dig backward, hide, climb trees, go nuts, or live in lava. Some dig, others crash into things, can hit distant targets with water spray, smash enemies, rescue people, spray fire, spin webs, or paint with their tails. They are full of energy. They dance, kick, give milk, have roars that can cause a volcano to erupt, can clean dirty water, eat dirt and mountains, explode, or wander through time.

They are the next level of Pokémon, and they are all that!!